Whose Fault Is It Anyway?

A Modern Fable About Six Sigma

ISBN 0-9705079-9-2

First Edition, March 2004

Rath & Strong Management Consultants
45 Hayden Avenue
Suite 2700
Lexington, Massachusetts 02421
Tel: 781/861-1700
e-mail: rathstronginfo@aoncons.com
www.rathstrong.com

Whose Fault Is It Anyway?: A Modern Fable About Six Sigma
by David Hampton

DESIGN/PRODUCTION
Jean F. Drew, *content graphics and layout*
Stephanie Boyle, *project manager*

Whose Fault Is It Anyway?

A Modern Fable About Six Sigma

by David Hampton

Prologue

Managers have to spend time working on their long-term strategies, the financial performance of their business, and the development of their people.

So it's not surprising that they are usually too busy to think about whether their business processes — the fabric of the firm — work as well as they should.

Meanwhile, the people who work for them tend to be preoccupied with how they are going to cope with the problems they face every day.

So it's not surprising that they are too busy to think about ways of preventing the problems in the first place.

And so things go wrong, with such regularity that correcting problems seems to become part of the very process itself.

༄

So far as we know, the company in which this book is set is fictional. But the events depicted are real enough — they happen every day, in companies all over the world.

Could there really be such a thing as a company like Forgiveness that provides organizations with plausible explanations for their failings, so that they can break the news gently when customers have been disappointed?

Perhaps there is. Who knows? Perhaps, one day, there will be.

Rise and Shine

Getting up is never easy for me. No matter where I put the alarm, I can always find the snooze button in my sleep, as instinctively as if it were some isolated part of my body with an itch.

To make matters worse, my annual performance review with Rob Slater will take place this afternoon (but not, my subconscious reminds me, if I decide to stay in bed).

It's not that I have done badly. In fact, I fully expect a glowing report. No, make that, I fully *deserve* a glowing report. But I know that I can't just sit there and say thank you; I owe it to myself to use the opportunity to take some control of my career. I should tell my boss where I want to go next, where I want to be in five years, that sort of thing.

And that's when the old questions start whirring round my head again: What is it exactly that I want to do? Do I even want to stay with Forgiveness, when the firm seems to have little idea how to regain its competitiveness? Why am I working in this crazy industry anyway? Shouldn't I be in a more down-to-earth field — like advertising?

The sudden shock of cold feet applied to the back of my thighs brings a new sense of urgency to my semi-conscious contemplation. I remember the wonderful idea I had a while back, which seemed so exciting when my performance review was weeks away, but now seems just a little scary.

I had heard so much about Six Sigma, and how companies that had used it were finally able to make a lasting improvement to their customer service. So I read articles and web pages; I even went to a conference and heard a succession of executives sing its praises. Six Sigma really seems to be much more than a fad…it's a permanent addition to the set of tools that managers can use to implement their business strategy.

But perhaps it was a bit silly to think that a lowly Finance Analyst like me could start a Six Sigma project on my own, and somehow persuade our management to adopt the technique across the whole company. Perhaps I should just sit things out and see what the next year brings. Yes, that's what I'll do.

The icy feet press themselves more insistently against my legs. Then, from under the duvet, comes my wife's sleepy voice: "Paul, don't forget you are going to ask Rob if you can do that Six Sigma thing today."

Sighing, I swing my legs over the side of the bed. OK, perhaps I will ask him after all.

The Big Idea

"A Black what?"

For once, Rob Slater seems lost for words. It's supposed to be easy to give someone an enthusiastic performance review, and he knew the subject would turn to my next development move. So he asked what I wanted to do next, expecting me to ask for an assignment in any one of a number of areas, but I have come up with a more original idea.

"A Black Belt, Rob. It's just the term for people that run Six Sigma projects."

"But Paul, we don't do Six Sigma here!"

"I know, but my point is that we should," I explain. "Six Sigma can tackle some of the most long-standing and painful problems the company has, and I don't think there is anything more valuable I could do than that. Besides, it will give me just the leadership experience I'm looking for!"

"But how could Six Sigma do all that for us?" asks Rob.

"Oh, sorry, I thought you were already familiar with it."

"Of course I am," replies Rob, a little too quickly. Then he adds, "But I won't complain if you just give me a little refresher."

This is it, speech time!

"First of all," I say, "Six Sigma is about improving customer satisfaction profitably. You are trained in powerful problem-solving techniques, and then you lead project teams that solve the causes of the biggest business problems, one by one. It's a very structured, disciplined approach — that's why the project leaders are called Black Belts, I guess — and I'm convinced it's exactly what this company needs."

"But Paul," he says with a sort of childish innocence, "you're from Finance — what do you care about customer satisfaction?"

I fold my arms and try to impersonate the withering look my wife gave me when I asked why she wanted to read the Wall Street Journal.

Rob smiles. "OK, OK," he says, "but really, don't you think our profitability is a higher priority than customer satisfaction right now? You know how far behind budget I am, and I really can't afford to have you burying yourself in quality initiatives.

"Besides, you know we already have lots of plans that are going to improve satisfaction. The new database screens will cut down the search time, we are going to increase the number of analysts and we are launching some great new products — all in all, I think perhaps we should wait and see what that does for us before starting something like Six Sigma."

I suppose it's about what I should have expected from Rob. He always has new initiatives starting up, but they never quite live up to their promise because he's so impatient for results that he skips all the essential groundwork.

"We have an opportunity to try out Six Sigma without any cost or risk," I say. "I could get the training and coaching from our parent company. They have a course starting soon and I'm sure they would be happy to help. But we need Charlie Anderson's OK for it to fly."

I slide a few pages of notes across the desk to Rob. "Here's a quick summary of what Six Sigma does, how it works, and the names of some Fortune 500 companies that are already using it successfully. All I ask is that you talk to Charlie about it, to see if he is willing to give it a shot."

Rob picks up the papers reluctantly and flicks through them with little apparent interest, although he pauses momentarily when he reads the list of industry leaders and the savings they achieved on the last page. He shrugs his shoulders.

"OK, I'll give it a shot, but like I said, you need to go away and think about a job where you can really make a contribution to our business."

As I leave his office, I can hear Rob muttering something about not needing a "Finance guy with a conscience."

An Offer I Can't Refuse

A month after my evaluation, I have pretty much forgotten about my proposal to Rob. So when I receive an e-mail from our CEO, Charlie Anderson, with the subject line "Paul Bowes — Career Planning", I am unnerved. Charlie says he would like to discuss a bold and exciting idea with me. Knowing how hard-nosed he is, my immediate worry is that this means they are sending me to Pensions. My spirits are low when I join Rob Slater in Charlie's office at the appointed hour, and to make matters worse, Rob is smiling. This is going to be grim.

"Have you ever heard of Six Sigma?" asks Charlie.

He takes my dumbfounded expression to mean "no" and launches into an explanation of how companies all over the world have been using it, not only to improve customer satisfaction but also as a way of changing the company culture, to make decisions based on data rather than intuition alone. Although Six Sigma started in manufacturing, it works just as well in any kind of business, he says.

Charlie picks up a gold model of a tower block, a gift from the building contractor's grateful CEO. He examines it with evident pride. "You know, when we set up Forgiveness ten years ago, it created a whole new industry. Everyone loved us. We could practically name our own prices and if our quality or delivery was a bit erratic, well, our clients just had to put up with it."

He catches my eye and his voice hardens. "But times change, Paul. Just Causes and Right Justified came along with very comparable services, and they have taken so much of our business, and cut margins so tight, that we are struggling to turn a profit. We can't rely on big-bang new products alone to save us — not even Ambiguity, quite frankly — because the competition will have something similar to offer within months.

"We need to tackle the effectiveness of our whole operation, to get back to our industry leadership position and get back to making decent profits. And we need a structured approach to do it, not just a series of bright ideas. So I asked Rob to find out something about Six Sigma, and true to form he had a report on my desk the next day."

Charlie shows me the report that Rob has prepared, and draws my attention to the list of companies already using Six Sigma on the last page.

"Six Sigma is a strategic commitment, so it has to be driven from the top of the company," he says, reading the words I had written in the opening paragraph of my summary for Rob. "I wasn't sure how to prove it would work in Forgiveness until Rob suggested that we use one of our brightest people to do a couple of pilot projects."

I give Rob a puzzled look. "I know this is a bit of a surprise," Charlie says, "but rest assured that you will get all the help you need. You will have a project team, who will give about ten or twenty percent of their time to the effort. That way you will have all the resources and local expertise you need to get the project done."

"And I will be your Project Champion," adds Rob. "That's a key role in Six Sigma projects, and I'll be going on a short course to prepare for it. I'll be responsible for your project's progress, I'll make sure you get the help you need, and I'll support you if there are problems that need extra management clout to overcome them."

Rob's cheek has left me speechless. No wonder they call him "Slippery Slater."

"If your projects are successful, they will give me just what I need to get the Operating Committee behind me for a full-scale Six Sigma implementation," Charlie says. "We need you to make it work. It's going

Setting Up Six Sigma Projects

PROJECT CHARTER

Six Sigma work is achieved through a series of projects, each of which is defined by a Charter.

This is a contract between the organization's leadership and the project team, whose leader is often referred to as a Black Belt.

The Project Charter clarifies what is expected of the team, which helps them to stay focused on the key priorities. It will usually contain:

- The business case for the project, including financial benefits

- A description of the problem to be addressed

- The goals of the project, including timeframe

- The project scope

- Team membership, roles, and expected time commitments

- Any additional support required

PROJECT CHAMPION

The Project Champion's role is to:

- Identify projects and determine their appropriate scope

- Select the Black Belt and team members

- Ensure adequate progress, helping the team to overcome obstacles along the way

- Support and encourage the team

- Promote the project and ensure that the team receives appropriate recognition.

THE PROJECT TEAM

There is no set size to a project team, but four to six members is typical. Although the Black Belt position is full-time, the other members' contributions are additional to their regular responsibilities.

The most important team member is the Process Owner — in other words, the person responsible for running the process to be improved.

to be a full-time assignment, so that you can concentrate on the projects without being squeezed by day-to-day problems."

That's music to my ears. "So what's my first mission?" I ask enthusiastically.

"I need you to help Rob improve the performance of our IT client division," says Charlie. "I don't know what's wrong with the people there! I'm sick of hearing clients complain about them. It's costing us business, Paul. Rob has a number of ideas already, but I think we should understand the causes of the problems more thoroughly, so that we can be sure that we are doing the right things to fix them."

I'm immediately suspicious that Rob will try to use my project to get his own ideas implemented. But I decide to live with it for now and see what the Six Sigma approach comes up with, so I just say, "Sounds good to me!"

"Wonderful!" says Charlie. "The training starts in two weeks in our parent company's Head Office, and your place has been booked. They did ask, though, that you both meet up beforehand with Jim Royston, who's the Master Black Belt they are using for the training. He will help you to make sure the project is set up correctly. Jim is an outside consultant, so I'm sure he will be pretty curious to find out what we actually do for our clients. There you go, Rob, your first task as Project Champion."

He passes Jim's business card to Rob, who looks a bit puzzled.

"'Master Black Belt' is just the term they use for a Six Sigma expert who teaches the Black Belts," I explain.

"Yes, right, of course," says Rob vaguely.

Charlie looks from me to Rob and back to me, and his freckled face breaks out into an enormous smile.

Everyone Needs Forgiveness Sometimes

Rob and I are both a little apprehensive about meeting Jim Royston, but he has an assured, relaxed manner that calms our fears about this new adventure. We ask him to explain more about what Six Sigma is, and why it has proved so successful.

"I guess it's the systematic approach, the thoroughness, that makes it so effective," says Jim. "Each project follows a structure that guides the teams through all the necessary steps, to make sure you fix the right thing, and permanently."

Rob folds his arms. I'd say he prefers the splash and dash approach: lots of publicity for all his new initiatives, after which he is never around to help us to fix the problems they've caused. So Jim hasn't exactly chosen the best sales tactic.

"It also helps you to manage the complexities of rolling out such a large initiative," continues Jim. "Six

Sigma isn't something that hides away in a specialist department; it will touch every part of the company.

"It involves training people in the various techniques involved, with their project work going on in parallel so that they can apply what they have learned straight away.

"These projects are chosen to make sure we hit the areas that will have the greatest impact on the business — which usually means focusing on the ones that are affecting the end customer. It's also important that they have a well-defined scope, to make sure that they can be completed in about six months."

"So how long does it take to turn the company around?" says Rob. "A couple of years?"

"Well, maybe that's a bit optimistic," says Jim. "There's no miracle cure for customer satisfaction, so Six Sigma requires a lot of effort. The transformation won't come overnight. But you will start to see a financial return quite quickly, often within the first year, despite the up-front investment in the training and…"

"…and consultancy fees," says Rob.

"Well, now that you mention it, yes," grins Jim.

"How come we end up with a financial return?" I ask. "Surely better quality costs more money, not less?"

"Actually, it doesn't," says Jim. "We're talking about finding and fixing problems, not spending money to work around them. It's quicker and cheaper to get the job done right the first time than to mess around repeating work. The projects also tend to find other sorts of waste that come as a complete surprise to management."

"But won't all those problems creep back in again?" I ask.

"Good point," says Jim. "We have to make sure that every improvement really lasts. So the Black Belts — the project leaders, in other words — have to prove two things: first, that the changes they made really have been effective; second, that they really are permanent. If we didn't insist on that, you could end up with a series of initiatives that evaporate as soon as you turn your back on them, or maybe don't ever work in the first place."

Rob is closely examining the company motto on his pen, "Forgiveness means never having to say you're sorry." He doesn't seem at all aware that Jim has just described Rob's own management style.

"Over time, the effects of a number of well-chosen Six Sigma projects will be dramatic," Jim continues. "It's like watching your children grow — nothing much seems to be happening from one week to the next, until you suddenly realize they're taller than you are. But it takes time and management commitment to see it through. So even though your approach of having one pilot Black Belt is a bit unorthodox, I am delighted that Forgiveness isn't just rushing into a commitment like this."

I notice that Rob is wearing his "I'll give it six months at the outside" smile.

Then Jim explains, somewhat apologetically, that no one in our parent company could tell him anything about Forgiveness, and asks about the company and its products.

"I'm not surprised you drew a blank," says Rob. "We have to keep a low profile because our clients are ashamed that they need our services, and they don't want people to know we even exist. So we don't advertise, our web site is exclusively for our clients, and our sales team all pretend they are funeral directors to make sure no one ever asks them about their work."

Now he really has Jim's attention. "So what do you make, exactly?" he asks.

"Excuses," says Rob.

"Your service is that bad?"

"Nope. But some of our clients' service is. They pay us to write state-of-the-art excuses for them. They foul up, they need a line that makes it seem like it's not their fault. So 'we're sorry the plane is late leaving, but the mechanic left his screwdriver in the number two engine' becomes 'we regret that, owing to minor technical difficulties with the airbridge, we are unable to begin boarding at present.' And if you do it right, people just accept it."

Jim doesn't seem sure what to say, but he can tell that Rob enjoys talking about his work. "What kinds of businesses are your clients in?" he asks.

"All sorts, really," says Rob, while I sketch out the structure of the company, filling in the names of the people that we are likely to be working with.

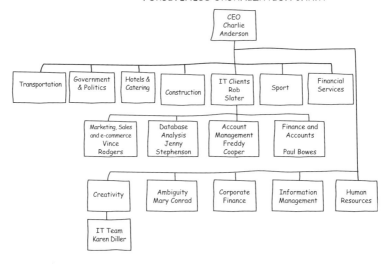

FORGIVENESS ORGANIZATION CHART

"Transportation, obviously. We're pretty big in hotels, construction, IT (that's my area)… we also help companies let their employees down gently, grovel to their insurers and explain themselves to the stock market… it's hard to think of a niche that we're not in, or an excuse that we haven't written. Oh, and I nearly forgot call centers!"

"We are very sorry for the delay in answering your call," says Jim with a smile, and Rob finishes the sentence for him, "as we are currently experiencing an unusually high number of calls."

Rob laughs. "I wrote that one myself in my first year here. Boy, has that earned a ton of money for us."

"But these excuses — I thought they were true!"

Rob raises his arms to the heavens. "But that just shows you how good they are!" he exclaims.

Eating the Elephant

My first week of training is hard work. I learn that a Six Sigma project takes place in five phases: Define, Measure, Analyze, Improve, and Control, which are often just referred to as DMAIC.

It all seems pretty logical: First you make sure you know what the customer's expectations are — that's in Define. You then quantify the current performance and identify possible causes of your failure to meet those expectations (defects, in other words); that's Measure. In Analyze, you use various analytical tools to figure out which of the potential causes are the most important ones, so that by the time you get to Improve you can focus your energy on just a few, and make sure your solutions really work. Finally, the Control phase involves preventing the problems from happening again, so that your results aren't a five-minute wonder.

This week we have covered Define and Measure in more detail, and now I need to apply what I have learned.

Regular sessions with the Master Black Belt are used to guide new Black Belts and keep the project on track, so I book a coaching session with Jim.

We start by going through the specifics of my project, and Jim helps me to draw a simple map of the process called a SIPOC diagram.

"There's a separate department for each type of client," I explain, "as their needs are all so different. Rob's group looks after excuses for accounts in the IT industry.

"We have a secure web site, maintained by Vince Rodgers, that customers use to place orders for new excuses. The orders are picked up by the Database Analysts — their supervisor is Jenny Stephenson. They check for errors or omissions and then search our excuse database for anything similar that we have done before, so that we don't waste time reinventing the wheel. If it really is a unique request they send it to Creativity, which is the group that develops the new excuses. Karen Diller is the team leader over there for IT accounts.

"Anyway, once a suitable excuse has been found or written, the job goes to the Account Management team, which is headed up by Freddy Cooper. They send an e-mail to the client with the new excuses and handle any follow-up issues that crop up."

SIPOC Diagram

SIPOC stands for Supplier – Input – Process – Output – Customer.

It is a simple diagram that is used to show the outline of the process to be analyzed. It helps teams make sure that everyone has the same understanding of which parts of the overall business process fall within the scope of the project.

For example, in this case the preparation of the invoice for the excuse is an important step but outside the scope of this particular improvement project.

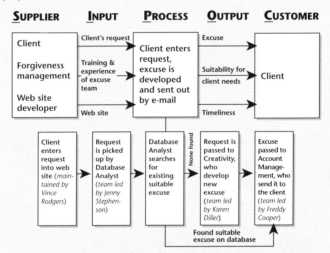

The inputs are both the physical flows of objects or information, and the other things (such as training) that are needed to make the process work.

The process itself may be broken out into slightly more detail, as with the five steps that are shown here.

The outputs represent the physical objects and information that the customer receives, and we also show here the characteristics of these outputs that are important to the customer.

In this book, the word "client" is used to represent the companies that use Forgiveness's services, to distinguish them from the client's own customers, who will be on the receiving end of the excuse in action.

"OK," says Jim when he has finally caught up. "So what's the problem?"

"It's your regular nightmare," I explain. "The clients keep rejecting the excuses we send them, so Creativity is asked to write new ones, and immediately blames the Database Analysts for not finding anything suitable, so they in turn blame the database system, and so it goes on. Not surprisingly, relations between Creativity and the Database Analysts are often pretty strained."

Jim is wearing a "been there, done that, got the t-shirt" smile, but I'm not finished yet.

"Don't forget that this is a company that makes excuses for a living, and we all love our work," I say. "Have you any idea what it's like, trying to get someone to tell you why something has gone wrong when they consider it a matter of professional pride not to give you a straight answer?"

That wipes the smile off his face.

"Anyway," I add, a bit more calmly, "with the client breathing down our necks for something better, we never seem to manage to get to the bottom of why it keeps happening. We spend most of our time making changes, the excuses end up being late, the database isn't reliable enough, our costs are out of control, there's bad feeling between the groups, the clients get the impression we are a shambles and they grumble about the web site — I don't know what that's all about — we can't get payment in on time, and…"

"Whoa!" says Jim. "You're expecting to fix all that at once?"

"Well, yes, that's what Rob wants."

"And how long will it take you to diagnose and fix all that?" Jim asks.

"Well, I suppose…," I begin, but I hadn't actually supposed anything yet.

"So," says Jim, "were you planning to fix things properly or just throw a bunch of initiatives at them?"

I shrug my shoulders sullenly.

"Paul, Six Sigma is about developing thorough answers to significant problems, not rushing in half-baked solutions to everything at once," says Jim. "So you are going to have to find out what the biggest issues are from your customers' point of view, and prioritize."

"I can imagine Rob's reaction when I tell him that Six Sigma is about the quality of the solutions and not the number of problems you tackle," I mutter sadly. "If he goes more than a couple of days without kicking off some new initiative, he starts getting restless and moody."

I'm beginning to wonder whether Six Sigma really can change the way we work that much.

We Learn to Listen
to Our Clients

After a week I have set up my team: Vince Rodgers, who looks after the web site, Jenny Stephenson from Database Analysis, Karen Diller from Creativity, and Freddy Cooper from Account Management.

I have also developed a Project Charter and agreed on it with Rob. This is a sort of contract that sets out the expectations of the project, both in terms of performance improvement and financial savings. Rob finally agreed in principle to narrow the scope of the project down to the excuses that are rejected by the client, which is his biggest headache — but only because I promised him that my next project would tackle all the rest of the problems! Oh well, one battle at a time.

The Charter also details who will work on the project, how much of their time should be needed, when we plan to complete each phase, and so on. It's nothing groundbreaking, just good project management discipline. But now that I think of it, for Forgiveness, good project management discipline isn't just groundbreaking — it's revolutionary.

At our first team meeting, I explain the basics of Six Sigma and ask everyone for their ideas on how we should gather details of our clients' needs and problems.

Freddy isn't keen. "We already know it comes down to the quality of the excuses that Creativity writes," he says. He seems to feel he has trodden this path before. "If you ask our clients what they want, they will expect to see an improvement, so it's best to leave well enough alone."

But Freddy does not have any actual data on what the biggest issues are, only his gut feeling. In fact, no one has ever actually asked our clients what is most important to them, or tried to find out exactly how they use our excuses. I point out that a key discipline of Six Sigma is to properly understand this kind of thing, and I persuade them in the end. We develop a plan to divide up the clients between us, and interview them over the telephone so that we can understand their expectations and priorities properly.

After a few days and a lot of phone calls, we reconvene to compare notes. The results are illuminating.

It turns out that few people quibble about the originality or inventiveness of our work (that will disappoint Freddy). Sometimes we accidentally include the word "sorry," which is strictly against corporate policy for some organizations (and all politicians), but this is easy enough to fix.

There are some bigger irritations, though: sometimes our excuses are totally inappropriate for the client's needs and have to be completely rewritten. Understandably, these types of mistakes really undermine our relationship with our clients, and we decide to make this the focus of our project.

Our clients also complain that excuses often arrive after the date we had promised, and they find themselves wasting a lot of time on follow-up calls to us asking where their excuses are.

These important requirements are termed, in Six Sigma speak, "Critical to Quality," or CTQ for short. We need to measure them, and we need to fix them.

We have now completed Define: the Project Charter has been set up, we have a common understanding of the process that we will focus on, and we now understand the clients' needs. Time to move on to Measure.

Measuring Our Performance

Before we start planning any improvements, we need to measure what proportion of excuses clients currently reject. It's easy to overlook this step, but doing so would be like starting a diet without weighing yourself first — you may feel as if you're getting closer to your goal, but you will never know for sure what you have really achieved. Actually, I think sometimes people do this deliberately!

I talk to Freddy Cooper and he explains that his team takes all the calls requesting changes, but nothing is ever recorded about how often this happens or what the causes are.

The only way around it is to get some willing volunteers to record the details manually, so I put on my nicest smile and meet up with the Account Management team to explain what I'm doing. Overall, they actually seemed quite pleased that we are going to try to figure out what has been going wrong.

They agree to track the change requests they receive — which client, which excuse, what type of excuse it was, what the problem was, how long it took for them to get the original excuse, and so on. This exercise will help us not only to estimate the size of the problem today, but also perhaps to pick up clues about some of the likely causes.

Our project team is starting to get enthusiastic now, and they soon develop the data collection forms and run some pilots to make sure that everyone is recording the information reliably and in the same way.

I also get the team to brainstorm the likely problem areas, and what they know about the causes. To structure our thoughts, we use a Fishbone Diagram — a simple tool for capturing the reasons for mistakes and breaking these down into possible root causes.

We start by thinking through why our excuses may not meet the client's needs. Before long, we have quite a good list: the brief from the Database Analysts to Creativity was not clear, the client entered the wrong information, the Database Analysts settled too easily for an excuse that's "close enough," or the excuse blamed the wrong thing.

I take Rob through this at one of our regular review sessions, and he likes the approach. However, he is quick to point out that he has already dealt with the last point.

Fishbone Diagram

A Fishbone Diagram is a simple tool for showing all the known causes and root causes for the problem being investigated.

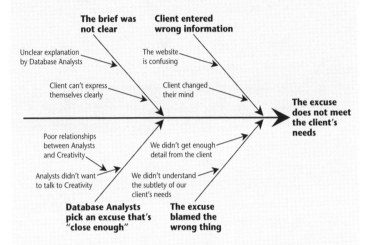

You read the diagram from right to left. At the head of the fish is the issue being analyzed: Here, the issue is "The excuse does not meet the client's needs." This is the starting point of the analysis.

Each major bone represents a possible cause, such as "Database Analysts pick an excuse that's 'close enough.' " You then ask why this happens and add further, more detailed bones for the root causes — in this case, "Analysts didn't want to talk to Creativity," to which a further underlying cause has been added: "Poor relationships between analysts and Creativity."

The best way to build the diagram is to ask "why?" repeatedly; this helps you to stay focused on the causes and not become distracted by symptoms.

This exercise enables the team to concisely capture all the knowledge they have about the potential causes of the problem; the diagrams usually end up being much more detailed than this simple illustration!

"Vince and I solved that a few months ago," he says. "The web site now asks the client to choose from three different types of excuse. A 'limited liability' excuse involves the client accepting some small amount of blame for the problem — for example, 'The server is down for essential maintenance work.' 'Beyond our control' excuses put the blame on natural causes, power supply interruptions and the like. Then there are the 'you klutz' excuses, which cunningly put the blame on the customer — for example, 'One of your drivers is corrupted,' or 'There is a conflict with unauthorized software on your computer,' that sort of thing."

Rob is, however, full of ideas to solve the other problems. "I'm concerned about the clients being confused by the web site," he says. "We redesigned it last month but I think the layout could still be improved. And we need to put quality checks on the excuses picked by the Database Analysts, to make sure they are only using excuses that match the client's request perfectly."

This is all very well, but if you launch into solutions without checking where the problem really lies, you can waste a lot of energy — and I've noticed that people that do this also tend to be a bit forgetful when it comes to checking whether their great ideas actually worked!

By now, though, I am used to handling Rob. I suggest that we hold off on these great ideas until we have seen the results of our data collection, so that we can show the evidence that will justify the cost of the layout changes and quality checks. Rob agrees to be patient for a while, and I set off with some relief for the next week of DMAIC training.

The Six Sigma Sleuths

Once you have generated a number of ideas about the possible causes of problems, the Analyze phase sets about narrowing down the field to the so-called "vital few" that we should focus our attention on. This is the detective work of Six Sigma, and the second week of DMAIC training introduces us to the graphical and statistical techniques that can be used.

The techniques are really powerful, but my head is soon spinning with them. Imagine being recruited off the street as a detective, with a week to learn how to do your job before being told to go and solve a murder: Who are you going to interview? What will you ask them? Where do you search for the weapon?

Jim Royston, my Master Black Belt, is really helpful, though. He helps me choose the right tools, and also helps me to get things in perspective: You need to use enough rigor to be sure your recommendations are sound, but the emphasis has to be on the results rather than endless analysis.

Back at Forgiveness, the mood is a bit downbeat, as the new football season has not begun well for us. We wrote less than a quarter of the explanations offered by the coaches of the losing teams, so there is bound to be an inquisition in the Sports Division.

I pounce on the early results from the data collection exercise. The analysts have found that an average of 6% of excuses are rejected by the clients for one reason or another. They have also collected plenty of circumstantial evidence; now I need to look for a smoking gun.

At the moment, I just have raw data. On its own, this won't help me understand what's going on — I'll have to interrogate it under bright lights before it will give me any information. It's not really complicated, just a standard spreadsheet and a statistical application. We use graphical analysis to visualize what is going on and, if necessary, statistical analysis to confirm or reject our findings.

I start by plotting the proportion of excuses rejected over time, and find that it varies between about 4 and 8%. There is quite a bit of natural fluctuation, but no unusually good or bad days and no visible trend up or down, so at least I know that our performance is more or less stable.

I try comparing the reject rate for each of our clients, but draw a blank here too: the difference is too small to warrant further investigation.

Using Graphical Tools

Graphs give us a much clearer picture of what's going on than columns of figures can. Here are two examples of how they can be used to show patterns more clearly:

TIME SERIES PLOT

This shows patterns over a period of time — trending up or down, for example. In the case of rejected excuses during the first 20 days of study, no patterns seem to be emerging.

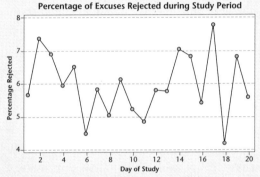

Percentage of Excuses Rejected during Study Period

PARETO CHARTS

Pareto Charts are used to compare the rate of occurrence of different types of problems — in this case, rejected excuses. They are sorted in order of frequency, and the resulting graph enables us to see whether or not the "80:20 rule" applies — meaning that a large proportion of the problems may come from a small proportion of the causes.

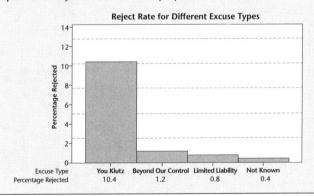

Reject Rate for Different Excuse Types

Excuse Type	You Klutz	Beyond Our Control	Limited Liability	Not Known
Percentage Rejected	10.4	1.2	0.8	0.4

How about the different types of excuse? Does our reject rate depend on what type of excuse we are asked for? It certainly does — I have my first big clue! Only (only!) 1% of the "limited liability" and "beyond our control" type excuses are rejected — but the "you klutz" excuses, where our clients imply that their customer is somehow responsible for the problem, have terrible performance — 10% rejects! This is pushing our overall average reject rate up to 6%.

Staring at the figures, I find it hard to understand how Forgiveness has missed this for so long. When you have the data in front of you, the pattern is easy to see — but of course, Forgiveness has never had this data before. Suddenly, I can see myself as a detective after all!

We have found the trail, and the project team and I begin house-to-house enquiries. We pull the details of the "you klutz" excuses that were rejected by the clients, and talk to the Account Managers to get to the bottom of the problem. There are a lot of stories to go through, and I'm glad I was able to narrow down my analysis before getting everyone down to this level of detail.

It's a chance comment that someone makes to Jenny that gives us our breakthrough. Sally, one of the Account Managers, told Jenny that her client had really blasted her a couple of weeks ago. He was launching a new high-speed storage device for home computers, and needed some way to handle the flood of service calls he expected to receive. He had asked for some "you klutz" excuses.

"The excuses we provided put way too much blame on the customer," Sally told her. "The client said that we sold him some brutal comebacks that made his customers feel guilty about the problem, when he only wanted to make them feel responsible for it!"

Wow. I never knew there was so much subtlety in the excuse business.

But there it was. Once we investigated further, we found that most of the rejected excuses came down to us not understanding how much of the blame was supposed to be put on the customer. And that's why it is so much worse in IT than in construction or retail or transportation, where it is so much harder to confuse people into taking the blame. We have found the culprit!

The Power of Data

Within a few days, my suspect has given a full confession. I checked out our excuse-ordering web page and found that clients choose which type of excuse they want from a simple menu, as Rob had said. But they have no easy way to indicate how much blame the customer should take. So they (sometimes) explain what they want in the comments box, and we (sometimes) read it. Not a very well thought-through process!

The third week of training, which covers Improve, comes at just the right time. We learn how to use designed experiments to statistically isolate influential causes when there are many different factors to consider. We also have a lot of fun learning how to brainstorm, generate innovations, and use influencing skills — and rather less fun learning how to develop timing plans, risk evaluations, and cost-benefit analyses. But it's good for us!

We give some of this a whirl in the weeks that follow.

Our first job is to convince Vince Rodgers that his web site needs to be changed, and I'm a bit concerned that he will complain about this because he only recently redesigned it. Jenny and I set up a meeting with him, and we carefully take him through all the data and the logic that leads to our conclusions.

I'm afraid to pause for breath in case Vince is about to say "yes, but…" before I have explained everything. So I'm a bit red in the face when I have finished.

But Vince just looks at Jenny and says, "We need to redesign the web site again, don't we?"

She stays very calm and replies, "Yes, Vince, we do. Do you want to put some ideas together?"

As the saying goes, "If at first you do succeed, try not to look astonished!"

While Vince and his team are developing the web site changes, I put together an announcement to let everyone know what we are doing, and think through our implementation plan.

I also work out the financial implications of reducing the number of excuses that have to be re-written because they didn't meet the customer's needs.

To do this, I use the figures for how much time it takes each month to handle the complaint from the client, re-instruct Creativity, prepare new excuses, and make sure the client is finally happy. I also have the numbers of rejected excuses that resulted in a full refund.

Many of the benefits are not quantifiable, though — we can't measure how much this project might increase our client loyalty or reduce wasted management effort and general frustration. I won't attempt to put a figure on these improvements because we are only reporting cost savings that we can reliably demonstrate — but I will still make people aware of them.

Fixing the Problem
for the *Last* Time

Week four of DMAIC training covers Control, and it seems like a new world to me. Not only do I have to analyze the problem with data and calculate the error rate both before and after the project — now I am expected to make sure that the process never goes back to the bad old days!

So we learn about standardizing work practices. That doesn't mean turning everyone into a robot; we will just concentrate on those things that really must be done in a consistent way.

And we learn that business processes, left to their own devices, tend to "rust." So we will use Control Charts, which are statistically designed graphs that enable us to spot when a process has deteriorated. They work by highlighting any deviation from the historical pattern that is too great to be explained by chance variation alone.

It makes me stop and take a deep breath when I realize that this Control stuff is probably the single biggest reason why manufacturing quality is normally so much higher than service quality. Manufacturing people have been measuring and controlling their processes for decades. In service industries like ours, though, people just do their job to the best of their ability. It is unusual for service industries to properly measure the quality of their results, let alone to have systems in place to detect gradual improvement or decay.

I book a coaching session with Jim Royston, and he helps me to think through what this should mean for our IT excuses. He also explains that I can't do it all myself — as the owner of this process, Freddy Cooper will be responsible for sustaining our improvements in the long term, so he has to take the major role in deciding how that should be achieved.

Back in the office, Freddy and I agree to set up automatic measurements of the number of times excuses are rewritten against the same job number. Freddy will include this in his monthly performance report for Rob.

There's a real buzz in the team now. The early results from our project show that we have reduced the rejects by more than we dared to hope, and even Rob seems quietly impressed.

I tell everyone it's time we shared our news with Charlie Anderson. That calms them down a bit!

The Acid Test

Charlie devotes an entire Operating Committee meeting to our report on the results of our first Six Sigma project, and the whole project team is there.

We are all fired up with enthusiasm for what we have done for the business, but as we take our seats I sense that one or two of the executives would rather spend the time talking about their problems than listening to our solutions.

Their frustration is heightened because Charlie has taken an urgent call from a Head of State who will speak only with the CEO. These guys don't have to use the web site, of course — when they have a crisis, they use the hotline for an instant expert excuse.

Charlie's advice is crisp. "I would blame it on unexpectedly weak consumer spending," he says. "That will do the trick... no, no, you don't need to say that... yes, of course... you are most welcome, sir, any time. Do give my regards to your wife."

He puts the phone down, and finally he is ready to hear from us. My throat is dry as I launch into my presentation — I know Charlie will leave me in no doubt as to what he thinks of it. I am well prepared, though, and everyone seems to follow the logic behind my conclusions.

Charlie absolutely loves the project. He beams at Rob, who looks pretty cheerful too. Removing the misunderstandings over the severity of blame to be put on the customer has cut the client rejects from 6% to just over 1%. As a result, the project has not only dealt with a major frustration for our customers, it will also save over $250,000 a year by reducing rework and refunds. Not surprisingly, Rob has also dropped his idea about putting in extra quality checks.

Mary Conrad has a tricky question for me, though. She is the head of Ambiguity, the new business unit that prepares evasive answers for politicians to use when they are being interviewed. "I've heard that Six Sigma is a sort of standard that represents almost perfect quality," she says. "You have reduced the reject rate to about 1%, which is wonderful, but that's nowhere near perfection, is it?"

"You're right," I say. "Actually, Six Sigma performance represents a defect rate of about three and a half per million. This is a demanding goal, and quite frankly in most service industries it is just not cost-effective to get there. At a minimum, it would mean doing multiple projects in the same area, progressively tackling the issues from biggest to smallest... or you may be better off using a technique called Design For Six Sigma to completely redesign the process.

"Alternatively, you can say, 'Thank you very much, that's one raging fire reduced to a few smoldering embers, let's move on to something else that is really hurting before we think about pushing for perfection in just one area.'"

Mary seems happy with this, but Charlie casually interjects, "What's your current performance level on your clients' Critical to Quality requirements, Mary?"

Mary calmly replies, "As you know, our customer needs are so diverse and confidential that you couldn't possibly put a single measure to them." Charlie nods sagely, probably congratulating himself on choosing someone as evasive as Mary to head up Ambiguity. Her time will come, though!

At the end of the meeting, Charlie asks me to stay behind with Rob. He thanks me again for straightening out the IT team — not a very kind choice of words, but that's Charlie. Now he is impatient to see another project. He reminds me that this would give him the evidence he needs to persuade the executive team to support a strategic initiative to launch Six Sigma. I have already been thinking about this and have a suggestion for them.

"We can't get IT excuses done on time, Charlie. Maybe a third of them are past our three-day turn-around promise, and many of our IT clients complained about it when we interviewed them. We all know the resource issues, but I am convinced that we can do much better."

Rob looks skeptical. "It only takes us about twenty minutes to completely search the database for excuses we can reuse," he says, "and with the improvements to the access screens already in place I can't imagine there's any more blood left in that stone. Creativity is turning the new excuses around in 24 hours, and with all the legal checks they have to make, that's probably as good as you can get. So I really can't see that there is much room for improvement."

But Charlie wants to give it a try. "Let's test Six Sigma all the way," he challenges us. Rob has nothing to lose, so he agrees and project number two starts to take shape.

Getting the Measure
of Our Delays

The next day, I meet with Rob to get some more background on the time it takes to develop excuses.

Rob is in a good mood because all the papers are full of Welton Electronics' disappointing full-year results. Welton is saying it is because their new Amenity chip was ahead of the market — which is one of our most profitable excuses.

When I finally have his attention, I ask him what measures he uses to manage the excuse-writing process.

"We know the average cost per excuse, broken down by client," Rob says, reluctantly putting down the newspaper. "Karen also tracks the number of excuses each of her creatives develops per month."

No surprise to find it is financial measurements that are the first thing Rob mentions when he thinks about managing the business.

"How about measurements on lead time for excuse development?" I ask.

"Well, we have records of the date each job passes on to the next stage, and we work out the average time for the database search and creative development each month."

"How about the backlog at each step?" I ask.

"No, we don't measure that."

"OK, so how about the whole lead time, from initial internet request to final e-mailing of a good excuse?" I ask.

"We tried that a while ago, but it was very hard to keep track of," Rob says.

"But Rob," I ask, "if you don't measure the whole process, how can you see things from the clients' point of view? We might have accurate measurements of how much time an excuse takes at each stage, but how do we know how long it spends just sitting in a job queue? Or what about the number of times excuses have to be redone because something is missing or wrong or whatever?"

Rob pauses for a minute, mulling this over.

"OK," he says finally, "I see your point. Thanks, Paul. You seem to be seeing things very differently since you had this Six Sigma training. Sounds like this will be a good project for us after all!"

Rob agrees to let me get everyone to record the time they start and finish each task on a spreadsheet, so that we can track the progress of each individual excuse through the system. They will also capture which jobs have to be done for a second (or perhaps a third) time, and the extra time that is spent dealing with this. At last, we will be able to see where the real hold-ups are.

Once this is clear, I get up to leave, but Rob calls me back.

"Paul," he asks, "you are pretty confident that we can be as successful in the future as we were with the first project, right?"

"Well, it's too soon to tell," I say. "But so many companies have had success with Six Sigma that I think we have every reason to expect it to work here too."

"And if you are a full-time Black Belt, and I get assigned as your Project Champion to have you work on a problem in my area, I won't be charged back for your time or anything, will I?" he asks.

"No, of course not." Where is he going with this?

"And I can get you and your project team to work on issues that I have in my annual performance objectives?" Rob adds.

"That's right, Rob."

"Fine. I just needed to be sure, that's all," he says.

He doesn't smile, but I can tell that he wants to.

✐

I decide to spend some time watching how the Database Analysts operate in practice. This is called "walking the process," and it's an excellent way to spot problems that have become ingrained in the regular way of working. My first victim is an irrepressible character by the name of Lisa Walczak, whose constant companion is a 32-ounce cup of soda.

As I watch her work, I am struck by the amount of time she spends going back and forth between screens, seemingly unfamiliar with the system. She tells me she has been in the job for two years, but the screens have been changed recently (the third time in six months) and she is still getting used to them.

After a while I notice that she is not pulling jobs from her queue in the order that they came in, and ask her about this.

"I'm going to get help on those when Jenny comes by," she says. "I don't really know what a — what's this one? — non-linear interface protocol — no idea what that is. Jenny will try to get Creativity to help with it, they understand all the latest stuff but they are often too busy to talk to her."

When I pay Lisa another visit later that afternoon, I notice that most of the backlog has cleared. "Yeah, I gave up on Jenny in the end," she says. "She's probably got meetings this afternoon. So I did the best I could rather than have them drag on into tomorrow. We have to meet our lead time commitments, so I try to finish the day with my backlog cleared."

I keep wandering around and watch some of Lisa's colleagues at their craft too. Two of them, Devadas and Angie, have an IT background, and seem to be more familiar with the technical side than the others. Everyone works hard, but some of them grumble about the new screens and all of them comment on the arrogance of Creativity. I take plenty of notes.

Faultfinding — or Merely Finding Fault?

Everyone on the original team is eager to be involved in the second project, so I gather them together and we go through my findings.

"The Database Analysts seem like a pretty good bunch of people," I say. "I was amazed at the complexity of the searches they have to do to find exactly the right excuse. I had no idea it was such an exacting business!"

OK, that's the flattery over with. But I do mean it.

"I also noticed that they struggle with the screens sometimes. Do you know why that is?" I ask.

Jenny explains that the database system has never been very user-friendly. "I've done what I can," she says, "and we have tried changing the screens around to make the sequence more logical, but what suits one analyst turns out to be awful for another, so we have never really found a design that everyone is happy with."

"Lisa also told me that they sometimes hold on to the more difficult requests so that you can help or get advice from Creativity," I say.

"Yes," says Jenny, "some of the jobs are a bit technical — it's nothing that needs any great expertise, but there are new products coming out all the time and we need help from Creativity to understand them."

"Which is all very well," Karen interjects, "but my guys really need to spend their time developing new excuses. It doesn't exactly help the flow when one of our brainstorming sessions is interrupted because a Database Analyst needs us to explain a new piece of hardware to them."

Jenny shrugs her shoulders and Karen folds her arms.

We agree to review the new lead-time data at our next meeting, to relate this to what I have seen while walking the process. But as the meeting breaks up, I can't help thinking that Jenny looks a bit uncomfortable.

ꝏ

A few days later I have the first few log sheets to play with.

Rob was right. The database search itself really is only taking about twenty minutes on average, though individual cases can take anything from five minutes to an hour, which seems odd. And Creativity never takes longer than 24 hours.

But now that I have details of the time it takes to get an excuse through the whole process, these individual times start to look like orchids in a field of weeds. One way or another, delays keep happening that drive the total time up to four or five days or even longer.

I'm particularly surprised at the number of excuses that have to go on some sort of detour before they are finished. Something will need to be checked with Creativity; Account Management will want the wording changed before the excuse is sent to the customer, and then the new database entry has to be changed too — it's hard work to get a picture of what is going on, even with all this detailed information.

I'm also a bit concerned about the approach that analysts have. When they get a job they don't understand, it goes to the bottom of the pile, and if someone does not help them out — which in any case adds considerable time and effort — they seem to end up guessing. They don't seem to think it is part of their job to find out things for themselves.

I try comparing the time taken by each of the individual analysts to find excuses. There is so much variation from one job to the next that it's hard to see the difference between the analysts. Their backlog also varies greatly over time, which makes it harder to see if anyone's is consistently worse.

I use Six Sigma's statistical tools to unravel these, and the result troubles me. Some of the analysts are much faster than others with the same experience, and I can't see a good reason why.

Devadas and Angie are significantly quicker than the rest — that is to say, even though the times for individual excuses in our sample vary widely, the difference between their overall average performance and that of the other analysts is large enough to prove that there must be a specific cause. Their backlogs are also shorter, and their excuses are less likely to be turned down by Account Management.

The statistics make the findings much more conclusive — I can prove it wasn't a case of, "Oh, they're not really better, you just happened to pick a few good ones." This more scientific analysis could come in very useful if people start to get defensive. Even so, the statistics can't give me an explanation of why there should be this difference in performance!

I made a promise to Lisa that I would try to fix the process, not point a finger at the people, and now I'm not sure how I'm going to make good on this.

The Use of Statistics in Six Sigma

If you tossed a coin 100 times and found you had 54 heads, you would probably not consider this to be a sign that the coin was biased.

On the other hand, if you had 90 heads out of 100, that would seem to almost guarantee that the coin is not fair.

But what if you had 60 heads? Or 70?

How much evidence would you need to conclude that the chances of heads and tails were not equal?

The business equivalent of this is to ask, for example, whether there is real evidence that one method is better than another, or whether one client experiences a problem more often than another.

Six Sigma can answer these types of questions using statistical tools that help us to distinguish between chance variation and an indication of a real difference.

This means that Black Belts are able to tell when an apparent difference in performance is really a sign that one group is better than the other, and when it is just a matter of luck.

One of the analysts told me that some of them were still using the old screen layout, so I run another test to see whether the new layout has made a difference — and to my surprise I found that it has not. The backlogs, the time to search for excuses, and the error rate are more or less the same for both. Again, I use statistics to work out how big a difference I need to see for it to be significant.

Although Jim Royston is much less involved now that I have completed my first project, I send him a friendly e-mail to let him know how things are going, and I mention my concerns about criticizing the individual analysts. I'm in luck — by the time I have fetched myself a coffee, he has written back and suggested that I investigate the reasons for the excuses being reworked.

I have already gathered this information from Account Management. They understand the IT business well, and are normally the ones that spot the problems. I do a Pareto chart of the reasons for the rework and notice immediately that two categories — "not technically correct" and "not appropriate for this problem" — seem to dominate everything else.

This is interesting, and reminds me of the problems I saw Lisa having when I went to watch her at work. I try grouping together all the more technically difficult

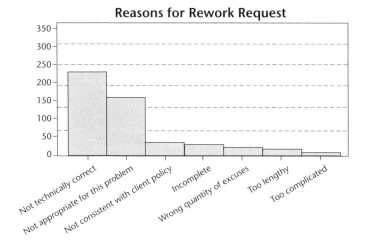

Reasons for Rework Request

(Categories: Not technically correct, Not appropriate for this problem, Not consistent with client policy, Incomplete, Wrong quantity of excuses, Too lengthy, Too complicated)

excuses and compare the lead time and error rate of these to the more mundane variety.

I find that the more technical jobs take longer to complete, are more likely to be passed back and forth between departments, and are more likely to be rejected by the customers.

I'm on to something!

Building Bridges

The team and I get together again and I take them through what I have found.

Jenny is very quiet. Well, this is her mess, after all.

Freddy has plenty to say, though. "No wonder we spend so much time going backwards and forwards!" he says. "The analysts are dizzy with all the changes to the system, they don't know a dongle from Adobe so they end up guessing, we spend all our time checking and we still get them wrong!"

We decide to get together with the Database Analysts to share our thoughts with them and involve them in brainstorming solutions. I put together a short presentation to explain everything to them.

❧

We reconvene the next day in a larger room called "Missy." It has a plaque on the wall in memory of a dog that, according to her young owner, managed to eat a history essay, a math test, and a homework notebook in one go.

The analysts seem fairly jaded as they file into our meeting. Lisa once mentioned to me that they have seen several improvement efforts in the past, but nothing has ever really made a difference. Most of them seemed to amount to just a lot of extra checks that management eventually grew tired of.

But when I first mention my surprise at the problems they were having with the layout of the screens, they find plenty to say. My problem quickly changes from getting them to talk into getting them to slow down.

Angie sums it up: "It seems like we flutter from one idea to the next. Every couple of months there are new changes, and they never really make things better — in fact, they just cause confusion. If we could only leave things alone long enough to get into a rhythm, we'd probably all be better off."

Needless to say, that's exactly what we agree to do.

We also learn that the analysts don't know what date the jobs are due. It seems there is so much focus on Creativity, because their work takes much longer, that no one ever thought of giving this information to the analysts. But so many jobs have already had one sort of delay or another that the analysts' queues turn out to be a mixture of routine and urgent jobs, with no way to tell them apart.

Jenny offers to put in a traffic light system — green for "routine," yellow for "priority," and red for "do it NOW!". This way the analysts will be able to see at a glance what to work on next.

Everyone is really in the swing of it now, and it is time for me to broach the delicate subject of some analysts performing better than others.

"I promised you I would focus on the process, not the people," I say. "And I will stick to that. So I am not going to name any names. But is there anything we could do to help level out the error rate? Maybe some sort of job aid?"

After a pause, Lisa dives in. "I'm probably one of the culprits," she says. "There are so many excuses that need to be found for some new program or new piece of computer equipment, and we are expected to find something similar in what we have done before, and I do what I can but with the best will in the world, sometimes I just have to take an educated guess." She shoots her boss an anxious glance but Jenny looks equally worried. "Lisa isn't the only one," Jenny says to me. "I think most people end up having to take a stab at it sometimes. I never thought it was leading to so many problems. I'm sorry."

Several of the analysts seem relieved to hear this!

We brainstorm a number of ideas for ways of improving people's knowledge — a technology display area, subscriptions to IT magazines, training courses, and update sessions with technically savvy people (though the analysts would all prefer these to come from Account Management rather than Creativity).

There are a number of techniques I have learned in my classes for helping a group to come to a consensus on which solution to choose, so I manage to keep them focused. Eventually we settle on a couple of magazine subscriptions and a monthly session with Creativity on new technologies and trends.

I manage to get everyone to see that, although the meetings with Creativity would be sticky at first, it would really help to improve the relationship between the two departments. I reassure everyone that the people in Creativity are no different from the rest of us, even if the guys do have rather long hair. Karen offers to set up a couple of half-day workshops to start getting all the Database Analysts up to speed.

The meeting ends with enthusiasm all round. "We've had these problems for years, you know," says Jenny. "We tried so many times to fix them that in the end, I just thought there was nothing we could do. But this time, I really think we have got it cracked."

She squeezes my arm and says, almost inaudibly, "Thanks, Paul."

Jenny's Fate

I'm back in the Operating Committee again. But this time it's not me who is presenting — it's Lisa. And she's really on a roll.

Lisa talks animatedly about the database search process, and how they struggled with the software and never realized which jobs were urgent. She shows them graphs depicting the time jobs spend in the Database Analysts' backlog; everyone is shocked when they realize that about 95% of the time a job spends in this area, it is not being worked on at all but is just sitting in a queue.

The analysts are at last getting more comfortable with the database screens, and the traffic light system is up and running. Lisa's eyes positively sparkle as she explains how much better things have become.

She also talks about the difficulties they used to have with new developments in the industry, and how the regular training sessions with Creativity have made a huge difference. Her enthusiasm is worth a thousand charts and diagrams. She refers to Steve Nakamura, who has conducted most of the sessions, as "my new best friend," and everyone laughs when she explains that, yes, the Database Analysts and "The Ponytail Club" really are on speaking terms now.

The managers love it. Getting Lisa to do the presentation was Jenny's idea — though Lisa is not slick at this kind of thing, her enthusiasm conveys how completely bought-in the team is, and that's much more convincing than a presentation by me.

Charlie is watching intently, and his jaw falls open as he takes in the significance of what we have found. When Lisa sits down, I sum up the project: "Charlie, the problems were not particularly obscure. It's just that we didn't know how to go about finding them — in fact, we didn't even know how to measure our performance, or know what was really important to our clients. These two projects have changed all that.

"As you know, there is a request on your desk for an additional two Database Analysts and a systems capacity upgrade. As of now, we're delighted to tell you they are not needed. Best of all, we will save $150,000 a year in refunds for late delivery."

The Finance Director makes a joke about the last time Rob hit his budget, and everyone laughs, including Rob — he is looking more relaxed than he has in a long time.

I wrap up by taking the group through the Control plans, so that we have confidence that the problems will stay permanently fixed. The traffic light idea, for example, makes prioritization an integral part of the process — much better than just instructing people to work on the most urgent jobs first.

We will also run quizzes for the analysts to check that the training sessions are remaining effective — that will help us make sure we don't fall asleep on the technology problem (I refrain from saying "again") in the future.

This is not very exciting stuff, which is perhaps the reason why, without Six Sigma, it is usually done so badly. But by now everyone really seems to want more and more, and at the end there is a barrage of questions about how to apply Six Sigma in other areas.

The meeting has gone an hour over schedule because of all the questions, but Charlie doesn't seem to mind. As people finally get up to leave, he motions to Rob and me to stay behind.

"Congratulations, Paul," he says. "Not only have you demonstrated that Six Sigma is going to work for Forgiveness, you also seem to have done my job for me in persuading the senior management as well."

The Control Phase

Introducing a new working process is rarely straightforward. People have become comfortable with the old ways, even if that means performing a great deal of rework, and there is a risk that they could gradually revert to the old methods.

The Control phase of a Six Sigma project addresses these issues. It involves taking whatever steps are felt necessary to make sure that the new process becomes the normal way of doing business, including measurements that can pick up any deterioration.

The key person is the Process Owner, who is responsible for the day-to-day performance of the process. Paul's Process Owner was Jenny Stephenson, and he worked closely with her to make sure that she strongly supported the analysis and the changes being made.

Here are two common techniques for ensuring the process remains stable:

Standardization and Documentation
Make sure that everyone is following the new process accurately and that all the key tasks are performed in the same way. Provide updated instructions and, if appropriate, job descriptions, performance objectives, and ISO documentation.

Process Monitoring
Six Sigma projects establish ongoing monitoring in the form of a Control Chart. This is a time series plot with the addition of one or two Control Limits (UCL and LCL, the Upper and Lower Control Limits). These are thresholds that, if breached, indicate that something has changed in the process. They are calculated from the ongoing process performance, so they are not the same as Specification Limits, which are set by customer requirements.

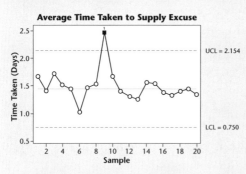

This Control Chart shows the average time taken to supply a sample of excuses. The ninth point is outside the Control Limits. This indicates that the process was not operating within its normal range of variation. The Process Owner is required to investigate the cause and take corrective action if necessary.

I pretend to be modest, but inside I am jumping on the table and punching the air.

Charlie lowers his voice and says, "I must admit I never had much time for the database team. If the clients weren't complaining, it was the analysts. I guess what you have shown is that it was actually their poor processes and control that dragged them down all along."

Then comes the sting in the tail. Charlie turns to Rob and says, "You told me last month that Jenny had really settled in well to that Database Supervisor job. But look at all the problems Paul has uncovered! Their work wasn't prioritized, the screens were a mess despite all the effort — and cost — that we've put into them, and half her team didn't even understand the technology. Are you sure she's the right person for that job?"

I groan inwardly. Rob hates to have anything tarnish his glittering image, and he probably wouldn't think twice about dropping someone that had become an embarrassment.

So Rob's reply astonishes me.

"Charlie, you will find that there are people like Jenny all over the company — people who muddle along on the strength of their relationships with their staff. And managers like us think the process is running as well as it can because we have never seen it working any better.

"And now this man comes along and he wants to look into all the problems we've been having. And I can tell you, Charlie, not everyone wanted him around, poking his nose in. I've had more than one anxious analyst in my office these past few weeks, wanting to know where all this is heading."

This is news to me, but I keep quiet.

"But Jenny had the courage to welcome Paul in and let him put her operation under the microscope. And, yes, the problems Paul has found are embarrassing for her. But she has helped him all along the way because she trusts us to do the right thing when we find out what's lurking under the stones Paul has turned over. Charlie, she is just the kind of person we need."

There's a bit of an awkward silence. I'm staring at Rob wondering if this really is the same guy that told me I should be looking for job where I could make a real contribution. Looking increasingly frustrated, Charlie finally rounds on me and demands, "OK, OK, but you just proved that the IT section was in a mess, didn't you? So whose fault is it anyway?"

Oh, how we hate it when we can't simply blame someone.

"Actually, Charlie, once you implement Six Sigma in earnest you are going to find this sort of thing again and again," I say. "We might like to kid ourselves that our operation runs like a well-oiled machine, but the fact is that most people in administrative jobs have to cope with these sorts of problems every day. Even if they know who to speak to, nothing usually gets done because people lack the skills to figure out the real causes. So eventually they just get tired of complaining."

After a minute, Charlie clears his throat and says quietly, "Thank you, Paul, Rob. I'm sorry. I guess I'm too used to blaming our problems on the people instead of the process. I'm going to drop Jenny a note and thank her for being our first guinea pig."

Now I know that Charlie really does get it.

Two Months Later

I have put together a document called "Lessons to Remember About Six Sigma," which summarizes the key things we have learned so far — partly to remind us what we should focus on, and partly to remind us what life was like before we started.

Setting up the full Six Sigma program, however, involves a lot more than this.

There is the task of selecting and prioritizing projects so that we make sure we are focusing on the key strategic business issues.

The Black Belts are carefully selected too, as theirs is a difficult assignment, but one that can make a tremendous difference to the company's performance. They (we!) are future leaders of the business, so the folks in the HR tower need to understand Six Sigma too.

I was delighted when I heard that Jenny had been chosen to attend the first "official" Black Belt training

Paul's Lessons to Remember about Six Sigma

We are only just beginning our journey to becoming a Six Sigma company, but already we have learned many valuable lessons.

Here are the most important ones:

- It is often difficult for managers to have a true perspective on the problems that affect their business processes. Generally, things are far less efficient than managers think they are!

- Processes with a great deal of variation or inconsistency are inefficient and difficult to manage. Six Sigma makes them transparent and smooth-running.

- Higher-quality processes actually reduce costs because there is less rework.

- Six Sigma projects involve a significant amount of structure, and a Project Charter has to be written. This should not be seen as a chore. It is simply good project management practice.

- Projects should be chosen to address a significant business problem, but within this keep the scope as narrow as possible — this helps to give the team a greater sense of urgency, and allows them to plan and execute improvements thoroughly.

- It is vital to understand your customers' needs properly, and very difficult to do this unless you actually ask them what their needs are.

- Measure your key business activities — and not only in financial terms. The measures that you use must directly relate to what the customer has told you is important to them.

- Statistical analysis can be very powerful when dealing with ambiguous data, or when looking for improvements against a background of varying performance.

- Don't blame the people. It is nearly always the process that is at fault. If you put good people to work on a bad process, you can normally bet on the process to get the better of the people.

program at Forgiveness. She is marvelous with people, she has courage and analytical skills, and her confidence has grown enormously as we have tackled the problems in her area together.

Many more people will be given simpler training and will run smaller projects, while still holding down their regular jobs. This helps the understanding and benefits of Six Sigma to spread more quickly through the organization. We call these people Green Belts (is there no end to the creativity of Six Sigma jargon?).

Then there are the managers of the business — they need to understand how Six Sigma works and play their role. In particular, those chosen as Project Champions will be active in selecting projects and helping Black Belts and Green Belts cut through the internal barriers to getting change implemented. Some will also go on to complete the training and projects that will make them Green Belts in their own right — including Charlie Anderson, who always likes to lead by example.

Finally, the rest of the company needs to understand the strategic commitment to Six Sigma, which means a major communications exercise.

Not surprisingly, then, we quickly realize that we need a consultant to help us think this through and to carry out the first waves of training and coaching. Jim Royston has proved his value already, and his firm gets the business.

Jim will hold our hands tightly at first, and then as we develop our own internal capability we will need him less and less, until we reach the point where we are able to handle everything with our own Master Black Belt. Which, by the way, will be me!

We will also need a full-time Six Sigma Deployment Director, a senior manager with the clout and the contacts to make it all happen. Rob is grinning from ear to ear when he informs me that he has asked for, and been given, this position.

"I guess I felt a lot of things were suddenly clicking into place for me," he explains. "I've been so frustrated, trying all sorts of initiatives to try to get some improvement in this business, but to be brutally honest none of them ever came to much. I just felt like I was spinning my wheels in the snow.

"But when I saw what you could achieve with Six Sigma, I realized that the problem all along was that we lacked a method for identifying the real causes of our problems before charging headlong into the improvements. And we had no way of making the improvements stick anyway.

"Now that we have Six Sigma, I really want to be part of making it happen for Forgiveness and putting us back on top."

Now that's what I call a conversion on the road to DMAIC.

⚬